Young
DREAMERS
PRESS

VISIT US ONLINE AT:
WWW.YOUNGDREAMERSPRESS.COM

CHECK US OUT ON FACEBOOK!
WWW.FACEBOOK.COM/YOUNGDREAMERSPRESS

This Book Belongs To:

Made in the USA
Middletown, DE
20 July 2023

35481110R00060